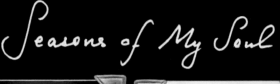

Rumer

Rumer

SEASONS OF MY SOUL

£14.95

Wise Publications
part of The Music Sales Group

London / New York / Paris / Sydney / Copenhagen /
Berlin / Madrid / Hong Kong / Tokyo

Published by
Wise Publications
14-15 Berners Street, London W1T 3LJ, UK.

Exclusive Distributors:
Music Sales Limited
Distribution Centre, Newmarket Road,
Bury St Edmunds, Suffolk IP33 3YB, UK.
Music Sales Pty Limited
20 Resolution Drive, Caringbah, NSW 2229, Australia.

Order No. AM1002661
ISBN: 978-1-84938-954-9
This book © Copyright 2010 Wise Publications,
a division of Music Sales Limited.

Printed in the EU.

Your Guarantee of Quality
As publishers, we strive to produce every book to
the highest commercial standards.

This book has been carefully designed to minimise awkward
page turns and to make playing from it a real pleasure.

Particular care has been given to specifying acid-free,
neutral-sized paper made from pulps which have
not been elemental chlorine bleached.

This pulp is from farmed sustainable forests and
was produced with special regard for the environment.

Throughout, the printing and binding have been planned to ensure
a sturdy, attractive publication which should give years of enjoyment.

If your copy fails to meet our high standards,
please inform us and we will gladly replace it.

www.musicsales.com

Am I Forgiven

Words & Music by Sarah Joyce & Steve Brown

1. I lost__ my heart. I did-n't know what to do.

*2° Instrumental till ***

I was so caught in mis-un-der-stand-ing I took it all out on

Come To Me High

Words & Music by Sarah Joyce

13

Slow

Words & Music by Sarah Joyce

Take Me As I Am

Words & Music by Sarah Joyce

23

Aretha

Words & Music by Sarah Joyce & Steve Brown

she's al-ways fight-ing___ some-thing in her___ mind.___

And it sounds like break-ing glass.___ I tell A-

-re - tha___ in___ the morn - in'. High on my head-phones and

walk - ing to school. I got the blues___

29

Saving Grace

Words & Music by Sarah Joyce

34

Thankful

Words & Music by Sarah Joyce & Steve Brown

2. Six o'-clock, sum-mer af-ter-noon,

next-door's kids are play-ing in the yard.

And I'm do-ing the dish-es at the win-dow and the ra-di-o's____ play-

-ing Su_-per-star.

And the sun__

38

39

that's where we laid you down.

And I can hear you whis - per

when the first frost falls on the ground.

You're a - live, just be thank - ful

Healer

Words & Music by Sarah Joyce & Gregory Churchill

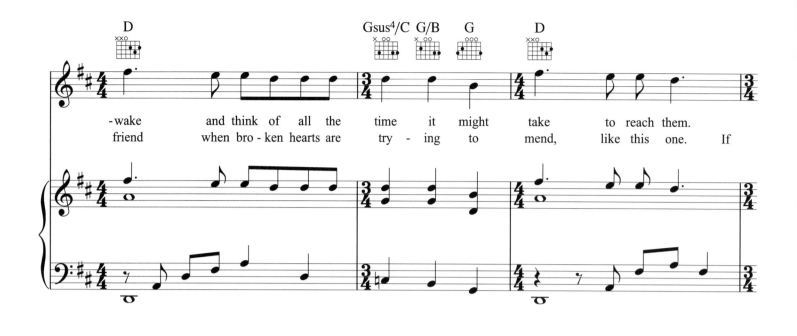

-wake and think of all the time it might take to reach them.
friend when bro-ken hearts are try - ing to mend, like this one. If

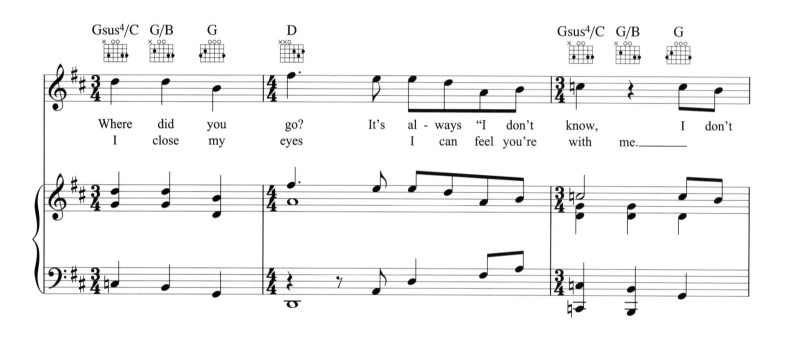

Where did you go? It's al - ways "I don't know, I don't
I close my eyes I can feel you're with me.

1° only

2° only

know."___ If

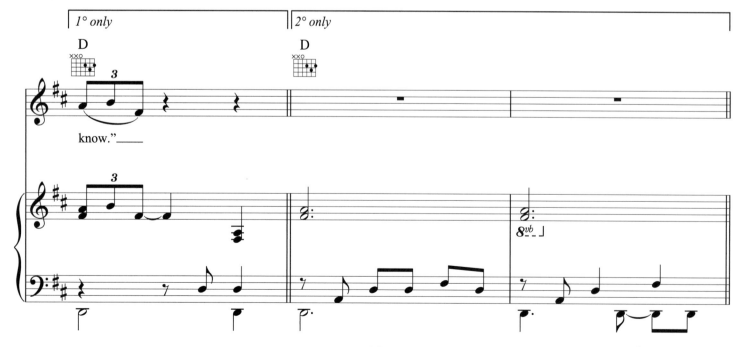

47

48

Blackbird

Words & Music by Sarah Joyce

50

hid - - ing?__ We've been through so much.

We've been through ev - 'ry - thing to - geth - er.__

We've been through so much. We've been through ev - 'ry - thing to -

-geth - er.____ Now there's a

On My Way Home

Words & Music by Sarah Joyce

1. Full of sor-row, I must have fol-lowed you here. Stood at the

4. When I wake up I see a fire red sky.____

And I____ get down on my knees in praise and dis-be-lief; is this beau-ty laid be-

Goodbye Girl

Words & Music by David Gates

1. All your life you've wait - ed for love to come and stay. And
2. I know you've been tak - en, a - fraid to hurt a - gain. You

now you're home at last.

Let me tell you, good-bye does-n't mean for-ev-

-er. Let me tell you, good-bye does-n't mean for-ev-